A Warwickshire Gospel

G000127335

A Warwickshire Gospel

Malcolm Monkhouse

YouCaxton Publications
Oxford & Shrewsbury

A WORD OF THANKS

It would not have been possible to finish this book without the help advice and encouragement of my wife Shirley, my daughters and Bob Fowke at YouCaxton. Heartfelt thanks – Malcolm

A Warwickshire Gospel' is a timely reminder that God comes to meet us in Christ, whether we live in Jerusalem or in Warwickshire. In this short book, Malcolm Monkhouse sets the Gospel of Mark in twenty-first-century Warwickshire and invites the reader to imagine what would that be like and how would we respond. Such an imagining is important and could stimulate fresh faith or even new faith. Why? Because the Christian Gospel is always for the here and now whoever we are and wherever we live. The author invites us to hear the Gospel afresh, to imagine Jesus with us now, here in Warwickshire. For those of us with faith, this is not imagination but reality. I hope that 'A Warwickshire Gospel' might stimulate not only the imagination of Jesus in Warwickshire but also the desire to know Jesus more.

The Rt. Revd. John Stroyan, Bishop of Warwick

Preface

This Gospel story is a deliberately free paraphrase drawing simultaneously on three translations from the Greek into English as its source. Readers of English are fortunately blessed in being provided with several translations into contemporary language. Well known and widely read are the Good News, New International and New Living translations for which the author is especially grateful. They are versions from which the core story can be retold in a completely different setting.

It does not purport in any way to be Scripture nor to be 'accurate'; it attempts to write what and how Mark would have written, in the sequence he wrote it, and to represent the events and the words that he recorded, all as if they took place in 21st-Century England. Mark writes his Gospel in everyday Greek and in the present tense (though almost all translators put it in the past tense) and this gospel follows his example.

Mark bases his Gospel on the testimony of Peter whom Jesus chooses as a 'rock' on which Jesus builds His church. The later Gospels of Matthew and Luke incorporate between them nearly all of Mark's Gospel, though at times with small amendments or omissions of the fine details that Mark includes in his fast-moving account.

.

1

Out in the fields by Draycote Water, a man called John has been busy for weeks on end baptising people from all over Warwickshire – villagers, town and city dwellers. (Actually it was prophesied 2600 years ago that a man would start doing this, but, of course, hardly anyone now remembers or believes things like that). Then one day a man called Josh comes to be baptised, and John knows something special is about to happen; he knows Josh, and he knows that Josh will himself baptise people, not with water but with the Spirit of God. Still, Josh steps forward to be baptised with water by John, and then when he does, the skies open, God's Spirit comes upon Josh, and God says out loud that He's utterly delighted with Josh.

But that's just the start. Josh is then taken off by the Spirit to a remote barren uninhabited island; he has to stick it out for six weeks on his own, being tempted by God's enemy, offered all kinds of escapes and incentives to switch sides - but Josh doesn't buy them. No, he survives all these trials and is thus totally fit to launch his mission; he's ready now to tell the world some great news – that God's New World, no less, is in prospect, and that he's going to recruit a team to learn from him what to do about it.

Yes, it's pretty radical and demanding stuff! But Josh doesn't go to London to draw up a job spec at a personnel agency in order to recruit his team. No, he just makes his way back from the island to Warwickshire, finds four ordinary tradesmen, asks them to follow him, and they do, just like that - packing up their jobs straight away. He doesn't offer them any money or even tell them where they are going. They just *know* it is utterly unique to be asked to follow him.

Anyway, he sets off with them and eventually gets into a church community hall in Rugby and starts teaching; and in no time at all he's accepted as if he was part of the official leadership. More than that, there's a man there who's sort of possessed, uncontrollable, and Josh deals with the problem so easily that people are staggered. The story gets in the local paper and spreads across the county and then gets on the Coventry and Warwickshire news channel. While this is going on, Josh and the four go back to the house where two of them (Simon and Andrew) live, and Josh cures Simon's mum-in-law of a terrible fever, and so quickly that she gets up, feels fine and cooks them all a meal!

That really sets things alight in Rugby. People come streaming to the house in the evening, wanting cures *and* wanting to watch it all. Josh heals a huge number of sick folk, and cures many of Rugby's serious drug addicts.

Next day, he's up before sunrise to escape to somewhere really quiet to pray. Simon and the others find him and want him to go back into the town but Josh says he must go to Leamington and the other towns in Warwickshire to preach to everyone; and off he goes, both preaching and healing and getting people off drugs and other addictions.

Next, a man with an incurable skin disease comes up to him and is healed immediately, because he believes in Josh, who really feels for this man and sends him off to hospital for them to do their own checks before he tells anyone. But he can't help telling people even on the way there, and the result is that Josh can hardly move for the crowds in Leamington, and he escapes to a few quiet spots in the country. Yet people still go out looking for him, wanting to be healed.

2

When Josh returns to Rugby, the crowds are huge, surrounding the house where he stays and preaches. Just to get to him, a man with an invalid in a wheel chair breaks open the back door, and Josh sees they have so much faith that he tells the invalid his sins are forgiven. This really upsets the regular religious preachers, but Josh tells them he has authority to forgive sins; and the invalid gets up and off he goes.

The onlookers are so amazed that they start shouting 'Thank God' and say they've *never,* ever seen anything like this.

Josh leaves for Draycote Water again and crowds follow him to hear him teach there. He spots a bloke called Matthew, who's been making a mint out of an agency he's got for the Inland Revenue, and asks him to join the team as an apprentice, and Matthew follows Josh - just like that! Then Matthew asks a load of folk from the crowd, including some dubious characters, to come round to his house for a meal. The regular preachers protest about these people being included in the party, but Josh tells them that it's precisely people like that who need to be helped. And so it goes on: whenever Josh helps the hungry or the misfits or heals on Sunday or disturbs their nice routines, the establishment gets really upset. He has to tell them that change is radical, that you cannot just make minor adjustments if you are going to bring about the New World of God's Reign on earth. You can't just patch up the old system - because it's bust. And Josh rankles them even more by showing them that he understands miles better than they do what God is saying in Scripture - on which they think they are the experts.

3

Not to be put off by any of this opposition, Josh then goes into the local church and heals a man in the building itself *and* on a Sunday. And that just about clinches it: the religious authorities meet up with the politicians to discuss how they can get rid of him altogether. Meantime Josh is off back to Draycote Water with, again, masses of people following him, and they are joined by crowds from Coventry and even as far way as Birmingham. Josh gets a boat organised so he can sit in it out on the water and heal and preach from it. And the numbers are still almost overwhelming, so he comes ashore and climbs a steep hill. There Josh gathers together the rest of his team of apprentices, twelve in total, including one called Jude Issington, who later on hands him over to the authorities.

Then he returns to the house in Rugby, and still there are crowds, including some high-powered theologians from London who have come to accuse him of using demonic power to drive out devils, which he points out, entirely logically, is a contradiction in terms. By this time his family want him to go back home and escape from the whole thing he's started, but Josh's message to them is that, as far as he's concerned, his family are those who are in the business of doing the work that God wants doing.

4

And he leaves town again to go back to Draycote Water and continues, from a boat by the shore, to teach the crowds with a whole string of stories about the new order of things. First, he tells a story which explains what happens when someone who understands what this new order (God's New World, his Reign) is all about, tries to get it across to others. The story goes like this.

Imagine a farmer, says Josh, going out to sow seeds on a difficult stretch of land which has stones, bindweed, shallow bits as well as decent soil, all mixed up. It's all that the farmer has to work on - where he is. He can't segregate the good soil, so he works hard sowing by hand as best as he can and then has to trust that the seed will produce a good crop in due course. Well, most of it doesn't; either the ground is stony and it doesn't root, or it is thin soil and the roots are weak, or they are choked with bindweed. But the deep weed-free soil yields a massive crop, up to a hundred times the weight of the seed he has planted.

Well that's the story, but the crowd cannot see what it means and even Josh's team of apprentices themselves cannot understand the meaning behind it, despite listening carefully. They don't see that the story is about spreading the word about the new order and not really just a farming story. That's because they still do not have the insight that comes from commitment to Josh and God's new order. So Josh tells them that the farmer is like someone who is spreading the message and the different types of ground are like different people in their response to it: only those who wholly accept it in their hearts will themselves go on to plant new 'seeds' and produce a great 'harvest'.

Having got this across, Josh goes on to stress that if you are really excited about something great, then you are sure to want to show it to other people. And key things are going to come to light, so it's vital that you stay on your toes, be alert and look and listen to what he has to say; then you'll begin to get some real understanding.

Equally, he says, if you don't keep listening, then you will lose whatever understanding you have. And having made that point, Josh turns next to provide some illustrations to describe the very nature of this Rule or 'Kingdom' of God, this New Order of things in the world. A farmer has to sow seed and that's his part of the job; but it is the earth itself that produces the crop, which is huge compared with the seed, and which the farmer harvests when it is ready. And one of the very tiniest seeds, the mustard seed, grows into one of the largest trees of all. Tiny beginnings; massive outcome - as long as we play our tiny part at the beginning, the New World Order will grow beyond our imagination.

Josh continues with many more stories and illustrations for the general public and explains them afterwards to his apprentices.

So it is a long day of teaching, and Josh then decides to pack up and go in the same boat with his team across to the far side of the lake as night approaches. He's tired out and falls asleep in the boat, and then suddenly a massive gale blows up and, in no time at all, there is panic as the boat takes in water. The guys wake him up thinking they'll drown out there in the middle, but Josh simply tells the wind and waves to calm down, and they do - just like that. Then he asks his men why they are scared. Why don't they trust him? They are baffled, and start to wonder who this guy, Josh, really is that he has such power over nature.

5

Landing on the opposite shore, they find themselves confronted by a bloke who is screaming his head off and looks and sounds deranged, as if he's escaped from an asylum and been wandering out in the open for weeks, and he has hardly a stitch on him. Then the guy drops down on the ground in front of Josh, and Josh drives out of him whatever had got hold of him. Some nearby folk, who see all this, charge off to Coventry and then people come out with them to see the man, who is now perfectly sane. They are so taken aback that they ask Josh to go away: they are scared by the sheer scale of change that Josh brings about in people. The bloke himself wants to join Josh back in the boat, but Josh tells him to go home to his home county and tell his friends what an amazing thing Josh has done for him. So through this guy, good news about Josh spreads through all the towns of Staffordshire (where he lives).

Crossing back over the water, Josh finds a large crowd again waiting for him. And among them the leader of a key local church casts all dignity aside and drops to his knees, begging Josh to go to his house and heal his dying daughter. On the way with the crowd following and pressing all around him, Josh feels a hand touch the edge of the special cloak he wears when preaching, and, on asking who did it, finds himself talking to a woman. She has a disease that is so horrible that she has no friends and no money because she's spent all she has on specialists. This is her last chance and she just goes for it, pushing her way to reach and touch the edge of his cloak. Her faith in Josh cures her instantly. While this is happening, the church leader gets a message to say his daughter has died and he tells Josh, who then just says 'trust me' and carries on to the house, and there he tells the crowd that the girl isn't dead, just sleeping. They laugh out loud. Josh tells them to stay put, goes in the house with the father and mother, takes the twelve-year-old by the hand and tells her to get up, which she does. The parents are overwhelmed. Josh tells them not to tell anyone what has happened, but just give their daughter a bite to eat!

6

Then Josh decides to move away for a while and goes off to his home town, Shipston. And there in the church he preaches - to the amazement of the locals, who cannot come to terms with how this woodworker's son, whom they once knew, can now preach as he does and do the miraculous healing they have heard about. They want nothing to do with him and refuse to believe in him - and without that belief he cannot do any miraculous cures for them. He does, however, lay his hands on a few other sick people and heals them, and then he leaves Shipston and goes off round the local villages.

And then he calls his team together to brief them for their tasks. They are to go out in pairs, with no resources, not even food, just a walking stick. They are to stop where they are made welcome and move on where they are not, leaving people there to their fate. So his apprentices go out, telling people to turn from their wrong ways, and they, like Josh, are able to heal people and rid them of the addictions and the evils that hold them in their grip.

Sadly, about this time, Josh's contemporary, John, who at the outset baptised all those people, gets himself bumped off by being involved with a very powerful politician who likes talking to John about spiritual matters but whose sleazy life John criticises to his face. It is actually the guy's own family who take revenge on John at a riotous party, but the police are not even involved and publicly the whole thing is blanked out, even though some people know about it and Josh is told about it by his apprentices. They have just returned from their first venture into 'on the road' work and report back to Josh on what they have done and taught: it is action learning for these apprentices!

They are certainly needed because the crowds press in on Josh wherever he goes. Even when he gets in a boat once more to find a much quieter lonely spot, the word gets around and he's besieged as he gets out of the boat. He feels sorry for all these people, saying they're like sheep without a shepherd, and he begins again to teach them. Time wears on and it's getting late, and the apprentices say that Josh should send the crowds off to buy a meal for themselves; but they're in for another bit of action learning because Josh tells them 'You feed the crowds'.

They say it will cost a mint to feed this lot.

Josh asks them what food is out there and they come back with five loaves of bread and two packs of tuna. Right, says Josh, all sit down in groups. Then he looks up to heaven and asks God to bless the food, and begins to pass loaf after loaf and chunk after chunk of tuna to the apprentices to give out to everyone. There is plenty for the five thousand men and their families; and they collect up twelve bag loads of crumbs and bits of tuna so as not to waste what God gives but take it for recycling as animal food.

Josh then makes his team go in the boat back across the water, while he sends the crowd home and goes up a hill to pray alone. It's night time by now and they are out in the boat and the wind gets up. Josh sees they are in trouble and about 3 am he comes out across the water on foot, and goes past them. They are absolutely terrified, thinking it's a ghost, but then they realise it is Josh. He speaks to re-assure them, gets into the boat and calms the waves. They are amazed. They cannot really believe all they have seen with the mass-feeding miracle and are trying to pretend it hasn't happened, and for a while they clam up inside.

When they arrive later on the shore, Josh finds more people, who recognise him and run off to bring sick folk on stretchers and in chairs from all around. And now wherever he goes in towns, villages, and on farms, the sick are brought to him to touch the edge of his cloak and be healed.

7

While Josh carries on his work of teaching and healing, a group of religious teachers come up from London to confront him about his teaching. Seeing that his apprentices are not complying with their age-old religious rituals which are meant to show how pure they are, they ask him point blank why his guys don't fall into line.

Josh doesn't answer their challenging question directly, but accuses them of hypocrisy and proceeds to give them a lecture about what God really requires, compared with what they are teaching. You teach, he says, that it's ok for people to tell their needy parents that they cannot help them financially because they must keep up the tradition of giving money to the church. This is in straight contradiction of God's command to honour your father and mother. In this way, you break God's law to protect your own tradition. And it's just one of umpteen examples of the same thing.

Then Josh calls up the crowd and declares: 'All of you, listen and try to understand: you are not made impure by what you eat, but by what you say and do.' Then he goes into a house to get away from them all and his apprentices ask him what he means by that, because they don't get it.

'Don't *you* understand either?' he asks. 'Look, food doesn't reach your heart; it goes through you and out the other end. Food isn't the problem. What makes you impure comes from within, from your own heart. That's where evil thoughts like sexual immorality, theft, murder, adultery, greed, wickedness, deceit, appetite for lustful pleasure, envy, slander, pride and foolishness, all come from; that's what makes you impure and unacceptable to God'.

And with that Josh leaves Warwickshire and goes up north to the coast, to an area full of immigrants who just don't fit in with British culture. He's after a bit of peace and quiet on his own for a while, but news of his arrival gets around fast, and an educated woman who has heard about him and whose little girl is distraught with evil, finds him and drops to the ground begging for help. Josh tells her he's got to concentrate on helping his own folk and not divert any resources for immigrants, but she cleverly argues that even dogs are given scraps.

'You're right', says Josh, 'and so I am right now healing your daughter.'

She goes home and finds her child lying in bed, completely cured.

And so it's back to the Midlands, this time to visit the Asians in Leicestershire. He heals a deaf man with a speech impediment in a quiet spot, but the news gets out, because everyone is so amazed, and they say that everything Josh does is so wonderful, even healing the deaf and dumb.

8

And Josh is then out there in the country with a great crowd, who have gathered waiting to see him for three days. They are hungry and there are no foodbanks nearby, and Josh feels sorry for them, and says some will pass out if they set off home without food. His apprentices ask where can they get food out here, but Josh just asks them how many loaves they've got. He takes the seven loaves, thanks God for them and breaks them into pieces for his men to give to the people. Then he does the same with a few bits of canned tuna. Some four thousand people are fed and there are seven bag loads of scraps left. Josh then sends the people home and gets in a canal boat to get down to Warwickshire.

On the way in Lutterworth, he again bumps into the religious leaders, who tackle him once more, this time to see if Josh is from God.

'Prove who you are - with a miraculous sign from heaven,' they demand.

Josh refuses: 'Why do you people demand a miraculous sign? I am not going to give this generation any such sign - period.'

He returns to the boat and continues the journey south. His apprentices discover there's only one loaf with them in the boat. Josh warns them to beware of accepting yeast from those religious leaders and from anyone who also exercises power over people.

'And why are you worried about not having any food?' he asks. 'Are you so dim? I have just fed thousands and did so only a few days ago. How many bags were left?'

'Twelve last time with the local folk we know and seven this time with strangers,' comes the answer.

'Right, yet you still don't understand what it's all about, do you?'

They continue, then leave the boat and walk to Dunchurch, where a blind man is brought to Josh, people begging Josh to heal him. Josh leads him out of Dunchurch and, placing his moist fingers on his eyes twice, restores his sight and sends him to his home, asking him not to go back to Dunchurch.

Josh and the guys then set off again, away from Warwickshire, and head for Oxford. On the way, he asks them what people at large say about who he is. They say that some reckon he is John, who is well known for all that baptising, whereas others reckon he is one of the ancient prophets, kind-of come back to life. Then Josh asks them who they themselves think he is. And Simon replies:

'You are God's anointed one.'

'Well, don't tell anyone,' Josh warns and begins to tell them what will happen. He will suffer terribly; he will be rejected by civil and religious leaders and be got rid of, killed - but he will come back alive. Peter takes him on one side and tells him not to talk like that. Josh turns back to all of them and upbraids Peter in front of them all for trying to offer him the easy way out instead of what God wants. Lots of people are gathering round and Josh calls on his men and everyone to listen.

'If you want to be my follower,' he says, 'you must give up your selfish aims, be prepared to suffer, and follow me. Try to keep your life as you see it, and you'll lose it; give it up for me and for God's New World Order and you will find true life.

Is it really worth losing your very soul, your true life, for the sake of gaining the world's possessions and comforts? And I tell you, if you are ashamed of me and my message to people in these wicked times we're living in, then I will be ashamed of you when I return to God who is my Father. Moreover, some of you here and now will not die before you see his Kingdom, his New World order, arrive with great power.'

9

The next week sees Josh taking just Peter, James and John up onto a hilltop in the Cotswolds. And suddenly he looks very different, his clothes shine so white like it's not real, and Moses and Elijah appear and start talking with Josh.

Not knowing what to make of this and scared like the other two, Peter shouts out: 'This is great. Let's make three shrines, one for you, Josh, one for Elijah and one for Moses'
– at which point a cloud comes over them all and from it a voice calls: 'This is my beloved Son. Listen to him.'

They turn around and Moses and Elijah have gone, leaving Josh there with them. He tells them to set off down the hill with him and not to tell a soul about what they have seen until he, the Son of Humanity, has died and risen from the dead. So they keep this to themselves but can't stop wondering what Josh means by 'rising from the dead', and they also start asking him why religious scholars keep going on about Elijah having to come before God's anointed-one can come, and Josh explains that Elijah has already come and was abused and ridiculed, just as he, the Son of Humanity will be, as the Scriptures say.

When they get down from the hill there's a crowd surrounding the other apprentices, who are arguing with some religious teachers. The crowd look up to see Josh and run to meet him, and he asks what's the argument about and a bloke says:

'Teacher, I brought my lad to you to be healed. He's dumb, got something evil in him that stops him talking and, worse, makes him fall over, foam at the mouth, grind his teeth, and can't move. So I asked your guys to get rid of whatever it is in him, but they can't do it.'

Josh says: 'You haven't got much faith have you, you lot! Just how long have I got to spend with you before you have some real faith? Bring the lad here.'

So they do and when he again goes into a spasm just as his dad described, Josh asks how long it's been going on, and the dad says it's been like that since he was a toddler, and he also says that it makes the kid fall over onto the fire or into water as if it was trying to kill the lad.

'Please help us if you can,' he cries.

And Josh says: 'What do you mean? Anything can be done if people have faith.'

The father replies: 'I do, I do, but help me not to have doubts!' And whilst the crowd is growing, Josh orders the evil spirit to come out of the boy and never return. There is a scream and the boy has another spasm and lies still on the ground, and all think he's dead, but Josh takes his hand and gets him on his feet. Later, when he's on his own, Josh's followers ask him why they couldn't do it themselves and Josh explains that that kind of evil can only be got rid of by prayer.

Josh and his apprentices now return to Warwickshire, looking for a quiet area where Josh can teach them, saying:

'The Son of Humanity will be betrayed and killed but will rise to life three days later.'

They just cannot make sense of this teaching, but are afraid to ask him about it, and so they move on - back to a house in Rugby. Josh asks them what they were arguing about on the road there, but they don't give him a straight answer because, in fact, they have been arguing about which of them is the best guy.

Josh sits down with them and says: 'Whoever wants to be number one must be last and serve everyone.' Then he gets a kid to stand in front of them, puts his arms round him and says: 'If you welcome a child like this on my behalf, then you are welcoming me, and if you welcome me, then you are welcoming my Father who sent me.'

John then tells Josh: 'We saw a man using your name to expel evil spirits, so we told him to stop because he's not one of us.'

16

'Well, don't stop him, because anyone who performs miracles in my name will not then slander me. Whoever is not against us is for us. And anyone who gives you a drink because you are one of mine will definitely be rewarded.

And if anyone makes one of these kids lose their faith in me, it will be better for them to be drowned. And if what you do or what you watch makes you lose your own faith, then just make it impossible for yourself to do it or watch it, because it is better to be held in God's New World order than to be separated from him for ever. Everyone will be purified with fire - just as salt purifies meat. Of course, salt is good but if it loses its flavour, how can you make it salty again? The salt of friendship is essential for you; live in peace with each other.'

10

Josh then decides to move on from Warwickshire to the South East and, as usual, there are crowds of people gathering to hear him preach.

Some academic theologians come along to try to catch him out. 'Do you reckon that it's OK for a man to divorce his wife?' they ask him.

Josh replies by going right back in history and asks them: 'What law have you been given?'

'That it is OK for a man to get a decree nisi and dump his wife,' they reply.

Josh tells them: 'You've been given that law as a cop-out because it's so hard to get you to understand what God intended from day one, when he made you, male and female, as it says in Genesis. And that's why men and women are to leave their parents, unite and are no longer two but one. And God has joined them, and they are not to be separated by man-made laws.'

In private the apprentices then ask Josh for more clarification, and Josh says: 'Anyone who divorces and marries someone else commits adultery.'

Then people bring children along for Josh to bless them. The apprentices tell them off and Josh gets real upset with them.

'Let the kids come to me,' he says, 'and don't stop them because God's New World belongs to people like them. I'm telling you that if you don't accept it as a kid does, you will not be part of it.' And Josh takes the kids in his arms, and blesses them.

Just as he is about to move on, a guy comes along and gets on his knees and asks: 'What, good teacher, must I do to live for ever.'

In reply Josh first tells him that no one is good except God, so he shouldn't call Josh good. Then he goes on: 'You know the commandments: do not murder, do not commit adultery, do not steal, do not testify falsely, do not cheat, respect and look after your father and mother.'

'Teacher,' he comes back, 'I have obeyed all these since I was a kid.'

Josh looks him straight in the eye, and says in a kind voice: 'OK, but there's just one thing you need to do: sell everything and give the money to the poor, and you'll be rich in heaven; and then come and follow me.'

The man just turns away looking depressed, because he's actually got lots of possessions and Josh looks to his apprentices and says: ' How hard it is for the rich to enter God's Kingdom.' And they are taken aback, but Josh continues: 'Listen everyone, it really is hard to enter the Kingdom, and it is much harder for a rich guy to do it than for him to get into 10 Downing Street without a permit.'

The apprentices are bowled over by this and ask each other who on earth can be saved. Josh eyeballs them and says: 'Yes it *is* impossible in human terms, but with God everything is possible.'

Then Peter pipes up: 'Josh, we have left everything to follow you.'

'Yes, I know' says Josh, 'but I can tell you that anyone who leaves his home and family and his work for me and my message of the good news of God's New World order will get more now in this age in return – more homes, brothers and sisters, children and property – but also more persecution; and in the coming age – will have eternal life. But many people who seem to be on top now will end up last in line, and those at the bottom now will be the first (in the Kingdom).'

Josh and his apprentices now carry on the way south towards London. He is ahead of them but they are apprehensive just like the others following behind. Josh again takes his twelve guys on one side to tell them what's going to happen. 'We are going to London where the Son of Humanity will be handed over to the powers that be. They will condemn him and let him be abused and disposed of. But he will rise to life three days after he is killed.'

Then James and John come up to Josh and say: 'There's something we'd like you to do for us. When you are with God in your glorious Kingdom, can we sit either side of you?'

Josh retorts: 'What! Do you have any idea what you are asking? Can you go through all the pain that I have to go through? Can you go through the baptism of suffering?'

'Sure, we can,' they say.

Josh continues: 'Then you will go through the pain and you will suffer that baptism. But it is not up to me to decide who will be beside me with God. He alone will prepare such places for those he chooses.'

The other ten apprentices hear about this, and are annoyed with James and John, so Josh calls them all together, and tells them: 'In this world, as you know, there are kings, presidents and other rulers, who have power over people. But that's the world; it's not how it should be with you. If any of you wants to be a leader, he has to serve the others; and to become number one, he must be a slave to all. For even the Son of Humanity did not come to be served, but to serve and to give his one life that many others might be freed.'

So they then carry on their way and, just as they are leaving Luton with a crowd following, a blind beggar called Bert is sat down by the road, and hearing that it is Josh who is coming along, he shouts out: 'Josh! Help me!' The folk round him tell him to shut up, but he just yells out again: 'Josh, please stop and help me!'

And Josh stops in his tracks and says: 'Tell him to come to me.' So they go and tell Bert to cheer up and get up. He throws off his coat, gets up and walks to where he hears Josh. 'What do you want me to do for you?' asks Josh.

'Josh, teacher, I want to be able to see again.'

'Then go on your way because your faith has healed you.' And right away, Bert can see and he joins the followers on the way (to London).

11

Continuing on the way, London comes into view as they reach Highgate Hill. Josh sends two apprentices ahead, telling them: 'Go to Islington where you will find an old bike tied up. Undo it and bring it. If anyone asks you what you are doing, just say the boss needs it just now and will return it right away.'

So they go and find an old bike just tied to a door, and as they start undoing the knots, people looking on ask them what they are doing; and they say just what Josh said to say, and people say 'OK.' They bring the bike back to Josh and put a cover on the saddle and some paper streamers on the frame and Josh gets on the bike. And the crowds who have followed are joined by loads of onlookers standing on the pavements, waving streamers they get from a market stall; and it all gathers momentum. People throw the streamers across the road and a groundswell of cheering and singing breaks out as Josh rides slowly on and on towards the city. 'Thank God! At last, this is it, he's arrived – the guy who's going to change the whole money-corrupted set-up. Go for it Josh!'

And then when he gets to the City, he has a quick look at St Paul's, just as night falls, and then rides off on a bus with his apprentices to Greenwich Village where they spend the night out in the park.

In the morning, on the way back into town, Josh sees a fruit tree in a garden, but there's no fruit on it, because it's out of season. But because Josh is hungry, he's upset, and tells the tree no one ever again will be able to eat from it. And his guys hear him say this to the tree.

Anyway, they carry on all the way into the City and arrive at St Paul's steps, and Josh moves into action against all the traders. He overturns stalls of church souvenir-sellers and pulls out plugs from money changers' computers; and stops people loading goods for sale in and around the church. He cries out to the crowds that have gathered around him: 'It is written in Holy Scripture "My temple will be a house of prayer for all nations", but you have allowed this whole area to become a place where financial swindlers can operate with approval.'

The religious authorities are soon told what's been going on and start thinking how they can get rid of Josh. But they are a bit scared because the crowd is listening and cheering as Josh speaks. And so the day eventually draws to a close and Josh and the guys quietly make their way out of the City.

The next morning, they're up early and walk past that fruit tree and see that it is now dead all the way down. Remembering what happened, Peter says to Josh: 'Look boss, that fruit tree you told off has died!'

And Josh says. 'Have faith in God. I'm telling you: if you go and tell a hill by the sea to throw itself into the sea and you don't doubt deep down, but believe that what God says will happen, then for sure it will be done for you. That's why I'm telling you also: ask and you will be given what you ask. And also when you are praying, you must forgive anyone you are upset with for what they've done wrongly to you, so that your heavenly Father will forgive you for what you've done wrong.'

Then they carry on walking into the City and on into St Paul's, where the religious authorities come up to Josh and challenge him:

'What right have you to be doing the things you did yesterday? Where do you get your authorisation from?'

Josh replies: 'I've got a question for you and if you can answer it, I'll tell you about *my* authority. My question is: where did John get his right to baptise from – from God or from a human being?'

They begin then to discuss how to reply: 'If we say from God, he'll then go on and ask us why we don't believe John, but if we say from a human being, we're stuck because everyone thinks John was a prophet (speaking for God).' So they end up saying to Josh: 'We don't know'.

So he says: 'Well in that case I'm not telling you what gives me my authority.'

12

And so Josh there and then resumes his teaching - with a parable. 'Once upon a time a man planted a vineyard, made a hole for the winepress, and put a security fence and CCTV in place. Then he got an agent to find tenants, and went away on a trip. When he was told the harvest was ready, he sent the agent to collect his share. The tenants beat up the agent and told him to clear off. So the owner sent another agent, and he too was beaten up, and the next guy who went was bumped off; and it just went on like this, till the owner couldn't get anyone else, so he sent his own lad, who was very dear to him. 'I'm sure they'll treat him properly,' he thought. But they said: 'If we kill the owner's son, we'll get the vineyard for ourselves.' So they did just that, and disposed of the body. Now what do you think the owner will do?' asks Josh.

'He's going to kill those tenants and get some new ones. Haven't you read what it says in Scripture? The stone which was rejected turned out to be the key one. This was God's work and a great sight.'

At this point, the authorities move to arrest Josh because they know that this story of the vineyard owner is aimed at them. But they hesitate because they are afraid of the crowd, so they turn around and leave the scene.

Then some theologians and politicians, sent to trap Josh with questions in front of the cameras, come up to him and say: 'Well now, you who keep holding forth, we know that you talk straight and you're not bothered with what people think nor what their position is, but instead preach about what God requires of us all. OK, tell us: is it against God's law to pay tax to the Government if we know it is being used in ways that break God's law? Should we pay it or not?'

Josh sees the trap straight away and replies: 'What are you up to? Bring me a coin. Whose face is on it? Whose name is on it?'

'Queen Elizabeth, Head of State,' they answer.

'Well, then, you pay the State what belongs to it, and you pay God what belongs to God.' And they are just speechless with amazement at Josh's answer.

Then along come some other people who are prominent in a Jewish religious movement. They are traditional but don't believe in any afterlife. They like legal arguments and are also trying to trap Josh so they launch forth with this conundrum. 'Teacher, Moses wrote this law: 'If a man dies and leaves a wife, but without children to succeed him, his brother must marry his widow so they can have children who can then succeed the man as if they were his children.

In a family of seven brothers, the eldest was married and died without children. Then one after another, the brothers married the widow, in each case dying before any issue. Then she died too. Now then, tell us: when they all rise up after death, whose wife will she be?'

Josh turns to them and says: 'You're wrong! You neither know Scripture nor the power of God. When the dead rise, they will be like the angels in heaven and they won't marry. And haven't you ever read the story of the burning bush? It says that God told Moses: "I am the God of Abraham, the God of Isaac, and the God of Jacob". He's the God of the living, not the dead. You are one hundred per cent wrong!'

One of the people present and listening to all of this is a professor from a big London theology college. Noting that Josh deals well with the previous questioners, he comes up to Josh and puts his own question: 'Which of God's commandments is the most important?'

Josh replies: 'The most important is this one: "Love the Lord your God with all your heart, all your soul, all your mind, and all your strength", and the second most important is: "Love your neighbour as you love yourself". No other commandment is more important than these two.'

The professor then says to Josh: 'Well done. You are right to say that there is only one Lord and there is no other God, and that we are to love God with all our heart, mind, soul, and strength; and love our neighbour as ourselves. This is more important than to offer sacrifices to God.'

Josh, approving of this guy's comment, tells him: 'You're not far away from God's New World, *His* Kingdom'.

Then Josh himself asks a question: 'Why do some of you theologians stress that being descended from David as King of Israel is what matters about the Messiah. David himself wrote a psalm (110) addressing the Messiah as my Lord.'

They don't know what to say and, after hearing all of this questioning and Josh's answers, no one has the courage to come up to ask Josh any more questions. And Josh can now, unchallenged, address the large crowd, eagerly listening to him as he teaches them:

'Keep your eyes on the religious authorities parading around in their fancy gear to be taken notice of, and getting all the best spots at ceremonies and big do's in the City. They use their position to extract money and homes from the poor and then make sure they are seen and heard saying long prayers. I tell you, they'll get a special come-uppance!'

And as Josh moves to sit by the boxes where people put money for the church, he sees that many well-to-do people put in several notes, but a poor older woman on her own puts in just two 50p coins. He calls his guys together and says: 'I know that this lady, who's actually a widow, has put in more than anyone. You see, they put in what they could spare, but she has put in everything she had, and will go hungry.'

13

As they leave the church, one of the guys says: 'Look Josh at these huge stones; it's a fantastic building, isn't it?'

And Josh replies: 'You see all these big buildings – well, I tell you, not one stone will be left standing on another; they'll all be brought down.'

Arriving now on the other side of the square, Peter, James John and Andrew privately ask Josh: 'Can you tell us when that will happen? What will signal it?' Josh sits down with them to explain at length:

'Don't let anyone mislead you. Lots of people will come, making out that they speak for me, saying "I am the one", and lots of folk will be taken in by them. When you hear of fighting near here and a long way away, don't panic. These things are bound to happen, but they don't actually mean it's the end of the world. Yes, nations and kingdoms will fight wars and there'll be earthquakes and starvation, but these are just like the pains before a child is born.

You're going to have to be on your guard. You will get arrested by the local police, taken to court and punished - because of me. You will find yourselves facing prime ministers and presidents, telling them about God's New World and his Reign. And this good news must be preached in every country. When you get arrested and put in court for this, don't worry before the trial about what to say; just say what God's Holy Spirit prompts you to say. Men will betray their own brothers and fathers their children. And the kids will rebel against their parents and get them bumped off. You will be hated because of me, but you will be saved if you stand firm to the end.

And the time is coming when naked evil will rise up to take over all power and desecrate the great buildings used so long for worship and government. When that happens, it's time to scarper to the hills. If you are outside your house, don't go back in to pack your things. If you're out working on a job, don't go home to get a coat. It will be horrendous for pregnant women and mothers with babies. Pray that it won't happen in the winter. Because I can tell you now, there will be days of greater horror than have ever happened since God created the world, and there will be nothing like them again. But God will limit these days of horror for the sake of His chosen ones.

And then if some one says: "Hey, look, here is the Messiah" or "that's him", don't take any notice. False prophets and false Messiahs will show up and perform miracles in order to deceive even God's people, if they get half a chance. So watch out! I'm telling you now before it happens.

After those days of horror, the sun will darken; the moon won't shine; the stars will disappear, and heavenly bodies will be shaken off course. Then all will see the Son of Humanity coming from outer space with power and glory. He will send angels out all over the earth and in heaven to gather all His chosen people together.

Now then, let's see what you can learn from the fig-tree. When its branches soften, green up and begin to sprout leaves, you can tell summer is on the way. Well, just the same, when you see the things happening that I've been talking about, you can tell that the time is near - about to happen like. And do remember, it's going to happen before this generation of folk have died. Heaven and earth will pass away, but my words will never pass away.

However, no one knows when this time I'm talking about will actually happen. The angels don't know, nor does the Son himself – only the Father knows. So watch out, be alert, 'cos you just don't know when it will be. It's like the boss going on a trip somewhere and leaving folk at home in charge, after telling them all what jobs to do, and checking someone keeps an eye on security. Well, watch out because you don't know when the boss will be back – it might be in the evening, or at midnight, or before dawn or when the sun comes up. You had better not be asleep! So what I'm telling you, I'm telling everybody – watch out for him coming!'

14

It's now just a few days before Remembrance Day. The civil and religious authorities are working out how they can arrest Josh on the quiet and do away with him. 'We'd better not risk disturbances and bad publicity this week-end, because it's a big public occasion.'

Josh, meanwhile, is down in Bethnal Green visiting Simon who used to have an awful skin disease. While he's eating, in comes a woman with a big jar full of really expensive perfume. She opens it and pours it over Josh's head. Some of the folk sitting there are upset and start saying: 'What's the point of wasting good stuff like that? She could have sold it for a packet and given the money to charity?'

And they start telling her off in no uncertain terms.

But Josh says: 'You just leave her alone! Why are you telling her off? She's done something beautiful for me. You will always have poor people and charities, but you won't always have me. She's done for me what she could, pouring perfume on me to anoint me, before I die and am buried. I'll tell you this: wherever people tell the world about God's New World Order, his Kingdom, they will also tell the world about what she has done in memory of her.'

The next thing is that one of Josh's apprentices, Jude Issington, goes off to see the top religious authorities to talk about how he's going to hand over Josh. They are really chuffed when he tells them and promise to reward him in cash. So he starts looking out for the best time to do it.

Preparations are now well underway everywhere for Remembrance Day, and Josh's apprentices ask him: 'Where do you want us to go and get ready a big meal for you?'

Josh tells two of them: 'Go to the West End, you'll see a guy carrying a big pack of mineral-water bottles and he'll ask you to follow him. He'll take you to a house, and there you ask the householder to show you the room where Josh and his guys are going to have this big meal. He'll take you to a big room upstairs, which will be already set up for the meal you are going to cook for all of us'. So they go and find everything just as Josh said it would be, and they get on with making the meal.

In the evening, Josh arrives with all the team. And as they are sitting round the big table having the meal, Josh says: 'One of you eating with us right here is going to hand me over.' Naturally they are all upset, and one at a time they say: 'Well, it's not me!' But Josh replies: 'Oh yes it is. One of you will do it, one who dips bread in the dish with me. I will die just as it was written a long time ago, but it's going to be terrible for the man who does it. He'll wish he'd never been born.'

And while they are all having their meal, Josh picks up a loaf of bread, gives thanks to God for it, breaks it up and passes it round to the guys, saying: 'Take it; this is my body.' And then he pours some wine into a glass, gives thanks to God for it also, and hands it to them, and they all drink from it. Then Josh says: 'This is my blood, being poured out for many. It's to seal the new agreement between God and His people. I promise that I will not drink wine again until I drink new wine in God's New World order.'

Then they sing together a song of praise and go out on a long walk up onto the hill in Greenwich Park. And up there, Josh starts telling them what's going to happen.

'All of you will scarper when the crunch comes, and you'll desert me. Remember what Zechariah the prophet says: "God will kill the shepherd and the sheep will be scattered". But after I am raised to life, I will go ahead of you back to Warwickshire, and we'll meet up again there.'

Peter then says: 'Even if everyone scarpers, I won't.'

And Josh replies: 'D'you know what, Peter? This very night before the cock crows twice at dawn, you will have told three people that you don't know me.' Right upset, Peter protests: 'I'll never say anything of the sort. Not even if I've got to die with you.' And all the others say just the same.

Carrying on walking, they get down the hill to a garden in the trees, and Josh says: 'Just sit down here while I go and pray.' He takes Peter, James and John with him, and suddenly feels acutely distressed. He says to them:' I am so torn apart inside; I feel crushed to death. Please stay with me and keep watch with me.'

Then he walks on a bit, and drops down flat on the ground and prays that, if possible, he won't have to go through with all the suffering he sees coming, but that somehow it can be avoided. 'Father, you can do anything. Somehow take this cup of suffering away from me, yet let me do what you want me to do - it's your will not mine.'

Then Josh walks back, and finds all the guys fast asleep. He says to Peter: 'Simon, What are you doing! Can't you stay awake and watch out for just an hour? And all of you – keep alert and pray that you won't be tempted, because you may have the right spirit, but you're easily tempted.'

Then Josh leaves them again to be on his own and prays once again - the same as he just did. And when he gets back, they're all asleep again and don't know what to say. When he comes back the third time, he says: 'Don't tell me you're still lying around and nodding. Well, that's just about enough! It's time. I, the Son of Humanity, am now going to be handed over into the hands of evil men. Get up. Here's the bloke who is about to do it.'

And as Josh says this, his apprentice Jude arrives with a group of armed guards, sent out by the civil and religious authorities. Jude had already given them a signal: 'You'll know which guy to arrest and take away when I go and give him a hug.'

So he walks up to Josh and cries out 'Hi, Teacher!' gives him a hug, and the rest of them seize him.

One of Josh's guys whips out a knife and attacks an official. Josh intervenes and asks: 'Am I a dangerous criminal that it needs armed men to arrest me? Why didn't you just arrest me outside St Paul's when I was speaking in public every day? Well, what the prophets have written about me must now come true.'

And all his apprentices run away and escape. Just one young man, a follower running behind in his pyjamas, is grabbed by the armed men, but he too escapes by leaving his clothes behind.

Josh is taken by the guards to a private house, where a group of religious leaders and legal advisers have got together in council. Peter follows at a distance and slips through the gate into the garden outside the house, to mix with the guards huddled together, as it's cold out there. Inside, they are trying to find solid evidence to convict Josh and get rid of him, but they can't. People testify against Josh to the council, but their statements contradict each other.

Then various guys stand up to say: 'We heard him say, "I will tear down this Temple made by men, and after three days I'll build one not made by men".' But they cannot come up with the same version of this story either.

So the leader of the council gets up in front of everyone and asks Josh: 'What do you say about these accusations? Come on, what's your answer?'

Josh says nothing.

The leader then asks him: 'Are you the Messiah, the Son of God?'

And Josh replies: 'I am and you will see me, the Son of Humanity, sitting by His side in heaven'.

The leader goes berserk, tears at his tie in horror and shouts to everyone: 'What more evidence do we need! You've heard him blaspheme. So what's your verdict?' And they all say that they need to dispose of Josh. And they start spitting at him, cover his face and bash him with their fists, and say: 'Guess who hit you, prophet man!' And the guards who are inside the room hit him as they take him away.

Outside in the garden, Peter is still keeping himself warm, when one of the women on the staff of the council leader looks at him closely and says: 'You were with Josh the Warwickshire guy in there, weren't you?'

'I don't know what you're talking about', says Peter, and as he walks across to the garden gate.

A cock crows.

The woman sees him there again and says to those standing around: 'This bloke is one of Josh's men', and Peter denies it.

A few minutes go by and then some of the others standing around say to Peter: 'You've got to be one of Josh's men, 'cos we know you're that man from Warwickshire.'

'I swear to God I don't know who you are talking about,' Peter answers back.

Immediately a cock crows again.

Peter remembers Josh's words: 'Before the cock crows twice, you will say you don't know me - three times.' And Peter breaks down and sobs his heart out.

15

First thing next day the whole council of religious leaders get together to decide what to do. They put Josh in handcuffs and take him off to the Mayor's private office.

'Look, are you in charge of this movement I'm hearing about?' the Mayor asks.

'Yep, that's me' says Josh. And the religious leaders pile in accusing him of all kinds of crimes, and the Mayor asks Josh: 'Well, what have you got to say for yourself?', but Josh says nothing, much to the Mayor's surprise,

And the Mayor doesn't quite know what to do. However, a tradition has grown up that the Mayor is allowed to release a criminal once a year if people in London ask him, and a case comes up at or around Remembrance Day. (He's not breaking the law; all the authorities understand this special mayoral 'parole'.) And this year there's a guy called Robinson in prison who's been accused of subversive activity against the Government but is actually quite popular. Being an adept politician, the Mayor decides to take a sounding in the various corridors of power and the media.

He asks them: 'Should I release this Josh bloke who heads up his so-called God movement, or that guy Robinson, who's in detention for subversion?'

He knows that Josh has been arrested because he's a problem for the religious establishment; and they lose no time in lobbying everyone they know to e-mail the Mayor, demanding he release Robinson.

So the Mayor then asks them: 'If I do let Robinson out, what do you want me to do with Josh then?'

'Just get rid of him!' the leaders reply.

'But,' the Mayor comes back,' what has he done wrong?'

And all the people he asks the same question to, say: 'Just get rid of him!'

So the Mayor, thinking about the next election and wanting to stay popular, issues an order for Josh to be done over in prison and taken to a military compound for the full treatment. He's stripped and dressed in a purple robe like bishops wear, and a hat with razor blades in it.

They salute him, shouting, 'Hey Mr Holy man, boss of your God movement.'

Then they bash him about, spit on him and drop on their knees, as if they're bowing down to him. When they get bored with this, they take off the robe and put his own clothes back on. And take him out for execution. (Increasing pressure from the public and the media in the face of insecurity and terrorism has now resulted in the return of the death penalty for various crimes against the state and the established order.) But he struggles to walk and on the way they meet a guy called Simon who has come up to London from the country, and they force Simon to carry Josh on his back.

They take them to the execution place called Skull Wharf. (It's a place where the public and press are allowed to watch from the gallery, a practice borrowed from those States in America that have administered the death penalty for decades.) Once in the chamber the guards try to get Josh to drink drugged wine, but he refuses. Then at nine a.m. they bind him on the bench and divide his clothes, which they have already removed, between themselves, using dice to decide who gets what. By the execution chair they stick a card with a felt-tip notice scrawled on it, reading 'Chief of the God Movement'. With him in the chamber strapped to execution chairs, one on each side of him, are two guys convicted of terrorist offences.

Members of the public already in the gallery are allowed to shout at Josh and they mock him, saying: 'You said you would destroy the cathedral and build it again in three days! What are you gonna do for yourself now, eh? Go on, get out that chair and save your life!'

And there also in the gallery are the leaders of the religious establishment, muttering to each other: 'He saved others, but he can't save himself. Let's see him get off that bench, so we can see and believe he is who he makes himself out to be.'

And even the two guys on the benches either side of Josh make fun of him. And this goes on and on and on, but at noon the skies blacken eerily, and they have to put lights on everywhere. It stays dark.

The lethal injection process takes hours, but at three o'clock Josh cries out: 'Oh God, why have you abandoned me?'

Some of the people watching hear him and think he's calling for the prophet Elijah. They get the prison guards to taunt Josh, offering a cheap coke to see if he can still drink and they say: 'Hang on a minute. Let's see if Elijah comes to rescue him.' Then Josh cries out loud a second time.

Some women are also watching. Among them are Mary from Middleton, Salome, and Mary the mother of James junior and John. They have followed Josh in Warwickshire and have looked after him. Many other women who came to London with him are there at the scene also.

Later on in the afternoon, a senior well-thought-of member of the House of Lords, Lord Joseph, turns up. He's been looking forward to the start of the whole New Order of things and goes straight to see the Mayor of London to retrieve Josh's body, because the week-end festival is coming up and all the usual funeral services will be closed. The Mayor is a bit taken aback because he doesn't realise Josh is already dead, and he gets a police sergeant to check it out. When the sergeant confirms it, he says that it's OK for Josh's body to be released from the execution chamber. Lord Joseph then arranges for Josh's body to be wrapped and placed in a stone grave set in a solid wall in the cemetery. Mary from Middleton and Josh's mother, Mary, are watching while this is going on in the cemetery.

16

After the festival, Mary from Middleton, James' mother Mary, and Salome go and buy oils and herbs to be used on Josh's body. Then they get up really early on Sunday to go to the grave. Walking up there they are asking each other, who is going to be able to open up this secure grave. When they get there, they see it's already been opened. They go and see a young man dressed all in white - and it's really scary.

But he says: 'don't be afraid. It's OK. You're looking for Josh whom they executed aren't you? Well, he's not here where they laid him, because he's risen up himself. Go and tell all his apprentices including Peter that he's left a message. You are to go back to Warwickshire. He's going to go back up there, and you'll see Josh there. Remember, that's what he told you!'

Absolutely terrified and shattered, they just run from the cemetery, not saying a word to a soul because they are so scared, until they get to Peter and tell him what's happened and about the message to go back to Warwickshire. Peter and his buddies are still in acute distress and tell Mary that they don't believe it. Josh then meets two of the other guys who have gone off out to the country. These two come back and tell the others, but they still don't believe it. So they set off for the hill in Warwickshire where Josh has told them to go.

When at last they see him, they fall to their knees before him, though some of them have not been able to believe in him. Josh comes right up to them and says:

'I have been given all authority in heaven and on this earth. So: go and find followers amongst all people in the whole world, make them apprentices, baptise them in the name of the Father, His Son and Holy Spirit. Teach them to obey everything that I have told you to do. You can be absolutely certain that I shall be with you till the end of this age.'

And Josh is taken from them to be with his Father in heaven. The apprentices go out and preach everywhere, and he is with them in spirit as they prove their preaching by the miracles they then perform.

LAST WORDS

Mark was the first person to write an account of the Good News of Jesus - 'The Gospel'. His account, the shortest, was for centuries treated with less respect than those of Matthew, Luke and John. Maybe that was because it lacks the long passages of teaching contained in Matthew and John and the birth accounts of Matthew and Luke (see below). Also, it contains less material that is specific to the history of Israel and the Jewish people. On the other hand, Mark bases his account very much on listening to Peter. It is mainly about events and encounters as distinct from discourse, reasoning, teaching and theological concepts. He describes events in the greatest detail of any of the gospel writers and often uses the Greek present tense to convey a sense of action and movement.

None of this is intended in any way to suggest that Mark's account is the *whole* story of Jesus's life, death, resurrection and teaching. It is all four accounts by the Gospel writers that constitute 'The Gospel'. (Those familiar with the scripts will also see that in the story above, the difficult end of Mark's gospel is replaced by the ending of that of Matthew)

What *this* 'Gospel' story, set in 21st century England, is trying to do is to help the reader, whether or not a follower of Jesus and whether or not a churchgoer, to re-think what would happen if God chose to be made man for us today, and to examine how would we respond to the call of Jesus today. If this story speaks to you afresh, you may wish to fill out further the story of the life and teaching of Jesus of Galilee, that hilly country with a lake, on the main trade routes, but regarded as provincial by the establishment of Jerusalem.

Matthew provides large chunks of the teaching of Jesus in Chapters 5 - 8 in the 'Sermon on the Mount', beginning with the eight 'Beatitudes' which describe what it takes to be truly 'happy' (blessed) and then providing many examples on the nature of the God's New World Order (His 'Kingdom') and the part we can play in it.

Luke covers much the same ground as both Mark and Matthew but also tells us about Jesus as a child and young man. Luke relates more of the parables of Jesus, notably the 'Good Samaritan' (Luke 10) which brings out what is meant by the commandment 'love your neighbour as yourself'; and 'The Prodigal Son' (Luke 15) which vividly and movingly brings out the meaning of *grace*. In the 'Acts of the Apostles', a separate document from his Gospel, Luke tells the story of the subsequent early days of the Church which *Jesus* is building (Mat 16:18) beginning with Peter – the 'Rock' – as leader, and the other apprentices.

John: finally, yet more of Jesus' teaching is to be found in John's Gospel, notably in Chapters 14-17, in which Jesus teaches and prays with His apprentices just before His arrest. Here he pulls many threads together about Himself and also gives his followers a New Commandment - to 'Love one another just as I have loved you'. There are thus three Commandments in the Gospel accounts, which are additional to 'The Ten Commandments'.

John, writing much later than Mark, stands back and paints a 'big picture' with general, almost philosophic, truths about Jesus and about life, death and eternal life. He concludes by telling us that if all the things that Jesus did were written down, the world could not hold all the books.

Printed in Great Britain
by Amazon